CW00847599

AMAZING, WEIRD, MIND-BLOWING FACTS FOR CURIOUS MINDS

AMAZING, WEIRD, MIND-BLOWING FACTS FOR CURIOUS MINDS

Sergei Urban

SEVEN DIALS

First published in Great Britain in 2023 by Seven Dials,
an imprint of The Orion Publishing Group Ltd
Carmelite House, 50 Victoria Embankment
London EC4Y 0DZ

An Hachette UK Company

1 3 5 7 9 10 8 6 4 2

Copyright © U-Studio Ltd 2023
TheDadLab is ™ of U-Studio Ltd. All rights reserved.

The moral right of U-Studio Ltd to be identified as
the author of this work has been asserted in accordance
with the Copyright, Designs and Patents Act of 1988.

All rights reserved. No part of this publication may be
reproduced, stored in a retrieval system, or transmitted
in any form or by any means, electronic, mechanical,
photocopying, recording, or otherwise, without the
prior permission of both the copyright owner and the
above publisher of this book.

A CIP catalogue record for this book is
available from the British Library.

ISBN (Trade Paperback) 978-1-399-620-65-9
ISBN (eBook) 978-1-399-620-66-6

Typeset by Hannah Beatrice Owens/Orion Books
Printed in Great Britain by Clays Ltd, Elcograf S.p.A.
All illustrations © Shutterstock

www.orionbooks.co.uk

This book is dedicated to my sons Alex and Max, for always being curious enough to ask 'why?' and being patient enough to wait while Dad googled the answer . . .

CONTENTS

START YOUR FACT-TASTIC QUEST HERE

HEY THERE!

I'm Sergei Urban. You may know me as that guy from TheDadLab who turned his kitchen into a colourful battlefield of baking soda and vinegar. I'm no Nobel Prize winner – far from it – so, why am I writing a book about everything from the microscopic wonders in biology to the gargantuan mysteries of space? Well, because I am incurably, irrepressibly, irresistibly curious. And you know what? I think you're going to love it.

Why? It's simple, really. If there's even a tiny spark of curiosity in you, this book will fan it into a bonfire of fascination. And who doesn't love a good bonfire?

If you're anything like me, you'll know that there's nothing better than the joy of discovering something new, especially when it's as surprising as the fact that you are, at this very moment, hurtling through space at the speed of 107,000 km/h. I know, wild, right?

But it's not just about facts. Oh no, my friend. This book is about rolling up your sleeves and getting your hands dirty (sorry about that in advance). And by dirty, I mean covered in squashed blueberries, food colouring or even homemade red onion juice, because every chapter is paired with an exciting hands-on activity.

These challenges are the perfect excuse for some quality time with your family and friends. Because shared moments of laughter, surprise and learning are priceless. But hey, if you're more of a lone ranger, that's fine too. You can still have a blast discovering and experimenting on your own.

So, are you ready to dive in? Ready to pull back the curtain and see just how incredible, strange and mind-boggling our universe is? Excellent! Let's get started. After all, if I – a somewhat clumsy, always curious dad – can get lost in the wonderful world of facts, you absolutely can too.

Enjoy the ride and don't be surprised if you feel your brain expanding at an alarming rate – it's just all that juicy knowledge settling in!

GIRAFFES CAN'T SWIM

Biology, the natural world
and real-life super-animals

➡ In 2018, a new human organ was discovered! Yes, another one! It's called the interstitium, and it is a network of compartments throughout the body that are filled with fluid. It plays a role in tissue structure and our immune responses, and it may even affect how our bodies respond to potential threats.

➡ When breathing through your nose, it may feel like you're breathing equally through both nostrils. Interestingly, this isn't the case – we only breathe through one nostril at a time, and often we breathe more frequently through one nostril than the other!

➡ Ever wished you were just a little bit taller? Well, although it's hardly noticeable, you are about 1 centimetre taller when you wake up in the morning than you are when you go to sleep at night! During your sleeping hours, when you are lying down in a resting position, the cartilage (a soft and bendy material in your body that helps your bones move smoothly) in your spine no longer supports your body weight and spreads out, bringing about this slight change.

- Did you know that your skin, the largest organ in the body (yes, it's an organ!), is actually very heavy? It accounts for approximately 15% of your total body weight! It's made up of three individual layers – the epidermis, the dermis and the hypodermis. Its thickness varies throughout the body, too. For example, the skin around your eyes and on your eyelids is the thinnest. It's thickest on your palms and the soles of your feet.

- When you develop a scar after being wounded, you might notice that this scarred area doesn't grow any hair or produce sweat. This is because regular skin has lots of special cells that scar tissue can't regrow. It's also less resistant to sun damage.

- It's not only snakes, frogs and dogs that shed their skin – humans do it, too. Every 28 days, the entire surface of our skin is replaced – not all at once, of course! We shed each skin cell individually over this time. This means you'll have about 1,000 skins in your lifetime!

- Like skin, our taste buds are also renewed on a regular basis. A single taste bud only lasts for ten days before a new one takes its place! Burning your tongue by eating foods that are too hot can also speed up the life cycle of taste buds, prematurely killing them off.

TEST THE SCIENCE NOW!

- Ever tried to lick your own elbow? If not, give it a try right now! It's impossible for most people to perform this seemingly simple task.

- It's also impossible to hum and swallow at the same time. Don't believe me? Give it a try right now! These two tasks cannot biologically be performed at the same time because, when we hum, we are actually exhaling air. Because our airways close when we swallow to avoid the accidental inhalation of food, the air can't escape to create the humming noise.

- If you can roll your tongue into a tube shape, you're one step ahead of some others! Many people never develop this ability. Try it now and find out if you can.

- Surprisingly, only about 30–40% of the population can raise one eyebrow without raising the other. Can you do this?

- How long is your tongue? Only around 34% of people are able to touch the tip of their nose or their chin with their tongue. Give this a try, and see if you're one of them!

- While it may feel like you lie awake in bed for a while before you drift into sleep, it actually takes only 7 minutes to fall asleep on average. Can you beat this time?

➡ Your brain is divided into left and right sides, or hemispheres. Interestingly, the left side of your brain controls the right side of your body, and the right side of your brain controls the left side of your body!

- The functioning of the human body is dependent on a good night's sleep. Our abilities are damaged after missing even one or two nights of sleep, but going just over ten days without sleep can even result in death! However, this is not the case for all life on Earth. Some birds that migrate only need a small amount of sleep over several months, and dolphins only sleep with one part of their brain at a time, meaning a part of their brains is always awake.

- About 60% of your brain is made up of fat. The rest is mostly water, protein, sodium and carbohydrates. This means that an intake of omega-3 fatty acids is actually very important for your brain functions.

- Every day, you take an average of 7,500 steps – that's about 5 kilometres. When you're 80 years old, if you've stuck to that amount every day, you'll have walked about 140,000 kilometres throughout your entire life! It would be equivalent to walking around the Earth at the equator approximately 3.5 times.

- The muscles in your body work like a secret team of superheroes without you even noticing! Performing tasks as simple as taking one step can put as many as 200 muscles in your body to work.

- It's true that bacteria can sometimes make us sick, but there are many types of bacteria that are healthy and good for the body. Just in your gut, you can find about 100 trillion of these helpful microscopic critters! These good bacteria help you digest food, keep harmful bacteria at bay and maintain your vitally important immune system – the system that stops you from getting sick. Even though you can't see them, don't forget that you've got an army of helpful bacteria working to keep you safe and healthy!

- DNA is truly fascinating! Did you know that we share 98.8% of our human DNA with apes? But then, you might wonder, how did we turn out so different? Numbers can tell us a lot about these crucial differences and how they came about. You see, 'base pairs' are important bits of information that determine the features of a living thing, and every cell in the human body has about 3 billion of these base pairs. Although only 1.2% of our base pairs are different to those of apes, that amounts to 35 million potential differences!

- You may be even more surprised to learn that we also share 60% of our DNA with bananas! Many of the genes that we use for simple, basic functioning are also found in many other types of plants.

- Scientists sequence DNA to understand the genetic code that makes each living thing unique. DNA does not last long – about every 1,000 years it loses 75% of its genetic information. That is the reason we do not have dinosaurs' DNA. However, the oldest strain of DNA we've ever sequenced was taken from fossilised mammoth teeth, left by mammoths that lived over a million years ago!

- You might think that massive blue whales or giant redwood trees would be the world's largest living organisms. Well, those guesses aren't even close! In fact, the largest living organism on Earth is a fungus known as the *Armillaria solidipes* (or honey fungus)! Its network, which grows in the Pacific Northwest, has successfully bagged this title. It covers a massive 9.1 square kilometres – that's roughly the area of 1,355 football fields! It's also estimated to be 2,000 years old.

- While we tend to think about mushrooms as plants, scientists that studied their family tree found that mushrooms (a type of fungi) are actually more closely related to animals than plants.

- Our eyeballs are one part of our bodies that don't grow as we do. They go through a brief growth spurt during the first two years of life and then stay the same size for the rest of our lives, with very little change.

- While you might squeal in both pain and delight when you're tickled by someone else, you might have noticed that it's impossible to tickle yourself. This is because your brain warns the rest of your body of what's to come, losing the element of surprise and reducing the tickling sensation.

- Did you know that you have more bones when you're a baby than when you're an adult? It's true – babies are born with 300 bones, but by adulthood, we only have 206. This is because some of the baby bones fuse together over time.

- There are some pretty large bones in your body, but the tiniest bones can be found in your ear. The smallest of these is just 3 millimetres long!

- Think bone is the hardest substance in your body? Think again! It's actually enamel – this is the substance that your teeth are made of. While this makes your teeth incredibly strong, regular brushing and dental appointments will ensure that this durable substance lasts a lifetime.

- Our bones might be heavy, but animals that fly can't afford all that extra weight. Budgies (short for budgerigars) are one such animal whose bones are, in fact, completely hollow, making them lighter, which makes flying easier. Some hollow bones are filled with air sacs that are connected to the bird's lungs. This structure helps birds take in more oxygen during flight.

- Compared to insects, modern humans have only lived on Earth for a very short amount of time.

While we've only existed here for 300,000 years, some species of insect have been living on this planet for 385 million years!

- Did you know that cockroaches can continue living for up to a week after their heads have been separated from their bodies? When a headless cockroach does eventually die, it's only because it cannot consume food or water without a mouth – it continues to breathe through tiny holes found in various places on its body!

- Ever had an itchy red bite left on your skin after you've been bitten by a mosquito? Those are all thanks to female mosquitoes, not male ones! While female mosquitoes bite humans and consume their blood, providing them with important nutrients to grow their eggs, male mosquitoes only eat and drink plant juices and decomposing materials.

- The patterns on watermelons may look random, but did you know that all watermelons have an even number of stripes?

- Trees that can talk? It sounds like the stuff of fairy tales, but for the acacia trees growing in African savannahs, it's true! These trees have been found to communicate with one another by emitting ethylene gas. So when an animal is chewing on their leaves, they immediately release these gases as a warning to surrounding trees that a 'predator' is nearby. The other trees then know to begin producing a special toxin to steer the animal away!

- Did you know that the eye of an ostrich is larger than its brain? It's true! This explains why, compared to other species of bird, ostrich might not be the most intelligent – but they do have impeccable eyesight. If we're talking big-brained animals, then the sperm whale takes the cake for the largest brain volume in the animal kingdom. Their brains can weigh, on average, 7.8 kilograms!

- While pigs say 'oink!' and cows go 'moo!', some animals are a bit more complicated. Guinea pigs, for example, make 11 distinct sounds. The most common of these is a high-pitched whistle or squeal, usually indicating excitement.

- Dalmatians are a beautiful, athletic dog breed known for their distinctive spotty fur. What may surprise you is that these dogs are born with plain white fur and only develop their spots after about one week.

- Giraffes cannot swim. Their long necks and legs cause them to become unbalanced in the water. Kangaroos, on the other hand, are surprisingly good swimmers. They use their legs and long tail to propel themselves along.

- Despite the name, killer whales are actually not whales at all! They're part of the dolphin family, 'Delphinidae', of which they are the largest member.

- On average, chameleons' tongues are twice as long as their bodies! In fact, their tongue is one of the longest and fastest in the animal kingdom.

- In the wild, giant pandas only live in China. But did you know that you can lease one? China offers pandas to zoos all over the world on a ten-year lease. However, it costs up to 1 million US dollars to house a panda for just one year, and any cubs born during this period are strictly property of China.

- Cat whiskers aren't simply there for decoration – they're actually extremely sensitive and can detect a change in the direction of airflow, as well as vibrations in the air. This sensitivity also helps cats to judge the distance between themselves and an object in their environment, helping them to navigate through a space.

- Ever seen a bird fly backwards? Probably not, unless it was a hummingbird. These tiny creatures are the only birds that can fly backwards and upside down! Unlike other birds, their wings are attached to their bodies with a ball-and-socket joint, which gives them a wider range of motion.

- While polar bears may be known for their distinctive white coats, their skin is pitch black! This black skin allows them to absorb more warmth from the sun, keeping them cosy in their Arctic homes.

- The glorious pink feathers on a flamingo are due to their diet of shrimp and algae which contain a natural pink dye. When they're born, they're grey or white, and only start turning pink when they're about one or two years old!

- Garden snails may seem harmless – and they are, to humans. However, they have 14,000 teeth hiding in those tiny mouths! These chompers are used for grazing and cutting their food and sit on the snail's tongue, rather than in their gums like humans.

- Taking down a large animal for dinner is quite a feat, so it's no wonder that leopards can be pretty possessive about their food. These killer cats are known to protect their prey by dragging it high up into trees, often leaving it there for days until they feel hungry enough to eat.

- One downside about fossils is that they don't show us the colour of a prehistoric animal's skin. While the fossil evidence we do have of dinosaurs shows that they did have different textures and colours, we'll never know what the colour of their skin was. When you see dinosaurs in movies and in pictures, their skin colour is merely a guess as to what they could have looked like.

- We suspect that dinosaurs lived pretty exciting lives, but they didn't live for very long. In fact, the oldest Tyrannosaurus rex that we know of lived to the age of about 30 before it died. That's approximately the life expectancy of a polar bear!

- The colossal squid, the largest animal in the squid species in terms of mass, has eyes the size of basketballs! The entire length of this enormous squid's body can reach up to 14 metres.

- The substance that our nails and hair are made of is the same substance that makes up the horns of a rhinoceros! It's called keratin, and it's a protein that our bodies produce naturally.

REAL-LIFE SUPER-ANIMALS!

- While they're not quite headless, barreleye fish certainly look like it! Their fascinating transparent heads allow them to look up through their skull and catch sight of both prey and predators that might be lurking above them.

- The hard-to-pronounce axolotl is a small, curious salamander that is famed for its ability to regrow any limb beneath the shoulder if lost. This works not only for their limbs, but also their spinal cord, heart and even parts of their brain! They can do this as many times as needed, without leaving any scarring, and the whole process can take as little as a few weeks.

- The phrase 'running around like a head-less chicken' was actually true for one very unlucky, but fairly famous, chicken back in 1945. When Colorado farmer Lloyd Olsen beheaded a chicken that became known as Mike, it miraculously continued to live for a further 18 months without its head! Mike became quite the celebrity and even went on tour.

- One of the world's toughest creatures is one you've probably never heard of. The microscopic tardigrade, otherwise known as the water bear or the moss piglet, can survive without water for up to ten years! It also has the ability to live through extreme temperatures as low as -273°C and as high as 150°C!

- While we humans cannot cheat death, there's a unique species of jellyfish that has almost achieved this superpower. A seemingly immortal jellyfish called the *Turritopsis dohrnii* has a clever trick to prevent ageing. It renews its cells completely whenever they become physically damaged or old, reverting them back to their earliest form, so that it grows into a whole new adult animal. This unbelievable power helps to make it biologically immortal!

- The blue-ringed octopus may only be as large as a golf ball, but it carries enough venom to kill 26 adult humans within minutes. Plus, there's no known cure for their venom, so their attacks are deadly!

- Professional boxers are pretty impressive, but even they have nothing on the mantis shrimp, famed for its powerful punch. These small, colourful marine creatures pack a punch that can accelerate up to 80 km/h in just a fraction of a second, making it speedy enough to vaporise water and generate a miniature shock wave!

- Stalk-eyed flies have a unique body feature that allows them to see around corners. Their eyes are propped up on two individual stalks, allowing them to work independently and giving the fly an incredible field of vision!

- Bats are known to have exceptional hearing and can navigate through spaces just by hearing how sound bounces off objects in their environment. They use something called 'echolocation', which uses sound to see! Bats make sounds that are so high-pitched that humans can't even hear them, and they bounce off things surrounding them and help them avoid bumping into these objects as they fly.

- When you first look at the thorny devil dragon lizard, you may think he has two heads. The large knob growing on its back is a fake head to confuse predators. Camouflage and spikes on its body give added protection.

- The platypus is an interesting mammal found only in Australia, and it has several unique abilities. Perhaps the most astonishing of these is the power to 'see' electricity, and use it to locate prey. The electric fields produced by the muscle movements in its prey can be spotted by the platypus – even when its eyes, ears and nose are all closed. It can help to track down even the most elusive animals!

➡ Your sense of smell is a huge help when it comes to recognising your favourite meal lovingly prepared by your mum! The tongue is limited when it comes to its ability to pick up on different tastes – it can only taste flavours that are sweet, sour, salty, bitter and savoury (some add cold and hot to this list). Your sense of smell needs to help it get creative, further enriching your tasting experience. The smell of the food is combined with your tongue's tasting ability to create layered and mouth-watering flavours. That's why your food might taste more bland when you're feeling sick or have a blocked nose – your tongue is missing its little helper!

ACTIVITY: THE FLAVOURFUL SENSORY ADVENTURE

Now that you've absorbed your first chapter of staggering facts about the wonders of biology and the body, it's time to put this new knowledge to use! Follow the instructions with a friend or family member and watch the nature of biology unfold before your very eyes.

Materials

- A pack of mixed-flavoured sweets (Skittles, Starburst, Haribo, or anything similar)

Alternatively, you can also try this experiment with other food types and flavours found in your home:

- Fruit juices (orange, apple, grape or pineapple juice)
- Herbs and spices (powdered herbs and spices like cinnamon, cumin, paprika or ginger)
- Flavoured snacks (crisps or snacks, such as barbecue, sour cream and onion, salt and vinegar or cheese)

Make sure that none of the people joining in with you have allergies to the ingredients.

Instructions

1. Wash your hands.
2. Choose one participant in your group to go first. This person must close their eyes (you can also use a blindfold or a scarf to make sure they don't see what they eat) and hold their nose closed with their fingers to obstruct their sense of smell.
3. Take out a sweet from the pack and place it in their hand. Their task is to eat the sweet and try to identify its flavour using only their taste buds and without the use of their nose and their eyes. Write down their guess on a piece of paper.
4. Now, we reveal the smell of the sweet, giving them a bit more of a clue. Allow them to stop holding their nose, but make sure they still keep their eyes closed. Ask them to guess the flavour again, and write this second guess down on the paper as well.
5. Finally, we uncover the mystery! Allow the person to open their eyes and find out the actual flavour of the sweet they've just eaten. Check their guesses on the paper – were they

correct on the first or second guess? How far was their guess from the true flavour?

6. From here, it's the next person's turn. Continue this activity until everyone in the group has had a few tries – and remember, this is a learning journey, not a competition!

Take it further

Have the group discuss their experience together.

- How did everyone's guesses change once they could smell the sweets?
- What does this teach us about how our sense of smell contributes to our tasting abilities?
- Were some flavours easier to identify than others? If so, why could that be?

There are no wrong answers, and every observation is valuable.

A SLICE OF PI

Maths, numbers and animals that can count

- The hour and minute hands on a clock face cross one another 11 times in 12 hours. This happens approximately every 65 minutes, not every 60 minutes, so it occurs only 22 times a day instead of 24.

- There is evidence of human beings using mathematics about 20,000–30,000 years ago in the form of markings on animal bones. The Ishango bone, an astounding archaeological discovery, shows tally marks carved into its side, which many believe is a sign that our cave-dwelling ancestors could understand basic maths and make primitive measurements.

- Roman numerals (I, II, III, IV, V, etc.) are a collection of symbols that the ancient Romans used to express the number sequence. Unlike our modern numbers, however, these numerals have no expression for the value of zero!

- Using mathematical probability (calculating how likely an event is to happen), it can be determined that, of 23 people in a room, there is a 50% chance that two of these people will have the same birthday.

- A billion is such a big number, but did you know there are 'illions' that come after it, too? A quadrillion, a quintillion, a sextillion, a septillion, an octillion, a nonillion, a decillion and an undecillion are all real numbers. When written out, an undecillion has a whopping 36 zeros!

- 'Googol' is a mathematics term that refers to a number that begins with 1, followed by 100 zeros. A number with a googol of zeros is called a 'googolplex', and is so large that it's difficult to comprehend it!

- The smallest functional unit of space in our entire universe is known as the Planck volume. This can be expressed as approximately 4.22×10^{-105} cubic metres, and it is often used in quantum physics. The Planck measure is named after Max Planck, a famed German physicist who contributed to the development of quantum mechanics.

- Graham's number is so large that it cannot be written out or even digitally expressed! This astronomical value is so vast that our observable universe is far too small to even contain any representation of it, assuming that each digit takes one Planck volume. Graham's number was named after Ronald Graham, a renowned mathematician, when it was discovered in 1971.

- When written out, you'll find that every odd number contains the letter 'e'.

- The number forty is the only number that, when spelt out, has its letters arranged in alphabetical order.

- 360 is a very prominent number when it comes to measurements, as 360 degrees is a full rotation. This also affects time because, when it was first recorded on the face of a circle, it became easy to divide units of time into 60 minutes and 60 seconds. But what makes the number 360 so special? The reason why historical mathematicians probably fixated on the number 360 is that it can be divided by 24 different numbers: 1, 2, 3, 4, 5, 6, 8, 9, 10, 12, 15, 18, 20, 24, 30, 36, 40, 45, 60, 72, 90, 120, 180 and 360. This means that we can split any perfect circle into a large variety of equal parts without having to use fractions.

- Ever heard someone say that they'll 'be there in a jiffy'? Well, it's not some made-up word – a 'jiffy' is actually a real unit of time. The exact length of a jiffy varies depending on the branch of science it's used in. For example, in computer science, it's 1/60th of a second, and in physics, it stands for the length of time it takes for light to travel 1 femtometre, or a millionth of a billionth of a millimetre! There are about three hundred thousand billion billion jiffys in a second! That's unbelievably fast!

- Pi (sometimes written as π) has a rich history and dates back to ancient civilisations. Historical Egyptians, Greek and Chinese societies all had ways of determining the value of pi, with the value becoming more and more accurate with time.

- A sequence of words is commonly used to help people remember the order of the first several digits of pi. This sequence of words is: 'May I have a large container of coffee?' Each word in the order has the same number of letters as the first eight digits of pi (3.1415926), which is usually used as its shortened value.

- Any pi fanatics can celebrate their love for the mathematical value on Pi Day, which falls on March 14th (3/14) every year. First celebrated in 1988 by physicist Larry Shaw, it has since become a popular and beloved annual celebration in many maths-loving communities.

- Next time you're playing your favourite board game, take a closer look at the die or dice. You'll be surprised to see that the numbers on opposite sides from one another always add up to seven!

- While the concept of infinity dates all the way back to Greek civilisation in the year 500 BC, the official symbol (∞) used to express it, known as the 'lemniscate', was first used by mathematician John Wallis in 1655.

- Numbers are infinite and complicated, and they can sometimes blow your mind! For instance, did you know that the sum of infinite numbers can result in a finite number? If you were to continuously add half of a number to itself starting from the number 1 (1 + ½ + ¼ + ⅛ . . .), you would never get an answer that amounts to more than 2!

- Have you ever heard of the Infinite Monkey Theorem? This states that, if one were to allow a monkey to randomly hit the keys of a typewriter an infinite number of times, the monkey will eventually type out the whole of Shakespeare's works!

- Percentages are reversible! It's true – take, for example, 50 and 8. If you work out 50% of 8 (half of 8 is 4), you can simultaneously find out what 8% of 50 is (also 4)! This trick works with any two numbers and can make calculating percentages much quicker and easier.

- 18 is the only number that is twice the value of its individual digits when added together. Add 1 and 8 together, we get 9. If we double 9, we get 18. This is the only number that works in such an equation!

- Prime numbers are special numbers in mathematics that cannot be divided perfectly by any other number except for themselves and the number 1. The largest prime number we currently know of has over 24 million digits, and the smallest one is the number 2 (it's also the only even prime number!).

- Ever wondered why a Rubik's Cube is so difficult to solve? It's because there are 43,252,003,274,489,856,000 possible combinations that can be made from the cube's many colourful squares, so finding just the right one is tricky and takes practice!

- Sudoku is one of the most famous mathematical games. The puzzle was first introduced in Japan in 1984, but it didn't become widely popular in the Western world until 2004. It has been calculated that there are over 6,670,903,752,021,072,936,960 ways to fill a 9x9 sudoku.

- You may know that chess is a complicated game that involves prediction, maths and concentration. But did you know that there are more possible iterations of a chess game than there existing atoms in the observable universe? In fact, if you multiply the number of atoms in the observable universe (10^{81}) by the total number of hairs on all the human heads in the world (10^{15})

and then by the number of seconds that passed since dinosaurs became extinct (2×10^{15}), the result will still be smaller than the number of all possible chess games (10^{120}). That is quite impressive for 32 pieces on a board.

- Evidence of mathematics can be seen in many instances in nature. One example of this is the shapes and structures that bees use to build their hives. Squares, triangles and hexagons are the three polygons bees could use, because they can be built side by side with no gaps in between them. But bees are highly focused on conserving energy and doing things efficiently, they chose to use the hexagonal shape to construct the cells of their hives. A hexagon has the smallest perimeter per area out of the three options, so making hexagon-shaped cells uses less wax and lower levels of energy from the bees. They also have the ability to calculate angles and make measurements, which helps in their building processes!

- Cicadas are another animal species that use mathematics. They are known to stay underground for long periods of time before they come out to mate, creating tunnels in their wingless forms and feeding on sap found in the roots of trees. Sometimes they come out after 13 years, and sometimes only after 17 years. Biologists have noticed that both of these intervals of time are prime numbers, and they believe that the cicadas have adapted to these particular life cycles to avoid predators that are more likely to have even-numbered life cycles.

➡ The Fibonacci sequence is a series of numbers in which each number is the sum of the two preceding ones. It starts with 0 and 1, and each subsequent number is found by adding the two numbers that came before it. The sequence begins as follows: 0, 1, 1, 2, 3, 5, 8, 13, 21, 34, 55, 89 . . .

➡ The Fibonacci sequence is often seen in nature – the number of spirals in a pine cone, the pattern on a pineapple, the arrangement of seeds in a sunflower and the number of petals in a flower.

➡ Concentric circles also surround us. Concentric circles are a set of circles that all share the same centre point but are different sizes, placing them perfectly inside one another. We can see this pattern in the rings of tree trunks, in ripples on the water in a pond and in the layers of an onion.

- The earliest known calculating tool that is still used today, other than our fingers, is the abacus. This device was invented in China, and its use dates back to 300 BC. Although it looks simple, it can be used to calculate additions, subtractions, multiplications, divisions and even calculations using decimal places. Some parts of the world still use the abacus today!

- A palindrome number is what we call a number that has the same sequence of digits whether you read it backwards or forwards. An example would be the number 21,312. We see such numbers all the time, but now you know what to call them!

- The idea that 13 is an unlucky number has roots in the Christian religion. On the night Jesus was crucified, 13 guests were present at the Last Supper, and many consider Judas Iscariot, Jesus's betrayer, to be the 13th guest. But many non-religious people also have superstitions around the number 13. Some buildings don't have a 13th floor, some restaurants don't have a 13th table, and some people will even go so far as to avoid getting married or buying a house on the 13th day of the month!

- One of the most popular numbers is 7. In a poll conducted in 2017, maths writer Alex Bellos found that, of 44,000 people surveyed, nearly 10% of them selected 7 as their favourite.

- Favourite and least favourite numbers tend to differ between cultures. For example, the number 4 is considered to be highly unlucky and symbolic of death in Chinese and Japanese culture.

- In Thailand, the number 555 is often texted to indicate that something is funny (it's the same as saying 'LOL' in the Western world). This is because, in Thai, 5 is pronounced as 'ha', meaning that 555 can be said aloud as 'hahaha'.

- The pattern on a football (or soccer ball in the US) is made up of pentagons and hexagons. You'll usually spot 12 pentagons and 20 hexagons.

- A number can only be divided by 3 if all of its digits added together equals a value that can be divided by 3. For example, 27 can be divided by 3, because 2 + 7 = 9, which is also divisible by 3!

- The ratio 3:2:1 is an easy way to remember the perfect cookie recipe! In this ratio, 3 parts will be flour, 2 parts will be fat (oil or butter) and 1 part will be sugar. Who knew mathematics could be so tasty?

- Did you know that there's a way to colour every single flat map in the world using only four colours, without any two adjacent regions sharing the same colour? This is called the Four Colour Map Theorem, and it was finally proven in 1976. Proving the theory was quite a unique process during that time as it relied heavily on calculations made by computers, which initiated topical debate about how computers could and should help in proving mathematical theorems.

ACTIVITY: THE FANTASTIC FOUR COLOUR CHALLENGE

Now that you have gained boundless knowledge about the fascinating world of mathematics, we can put you and your family and friends to the test during this fun, challenging and creative task! After all, you don't need years of study or a fancy qualification to enjoy maths.

The activity described below exemplifies a mathematical theory called the Four Colour Map Theorem. While it took over 100 years to prove, mathematicians have devised a theory that states that any map in the world requires only four colours to be filled in so that no two adjacent regions share the same colour. Today, we'll try it out for ourselves and see if it's true!

Materials

- A few sheets of white paper (or cardboard)
- Four different coloured markers or crayons
- A pencil and an eraser

Instructions

1. We begin with a fun, creative drawing session. Start by drawing a large map on your sheet of paper with a pencil – this can be a map of your neighbourhood, your town or an imaginary world.
2. Now for the fun part! It's time to colour in your map, but there's a catch – you only have four colours, and no two areas (countries or regions on your map) that share a side can be the same colour. The borders of two areas sharing a colour can touch at a point, but if they share an entire side, they need to be different colours. Can you manage it?
3. When everyone has completed their maps, have a look around and see if anyone has found a map that they think breaks the Four Colour Map Theorem. Check them all together.

Take it further

For an extra challenge, it's worth trying to create a map that you think would need more than four colours to fill in. If you think you've designed one, let someone else have a go at colouring your map and see if they can colour it in with only the four colours.

IT'S ELEMENTAL

Chemistry, atoms and 2,000 helium balloons

- You've heard of Ironman, but if there was a superhero named 'Steelman', he'd be much stronger! Steel is around 1,000 times stronger than iron in its purest form.

- It is estimated that 90% of the visible universe is made up of hydrogen! It is also the only element with no neutrons, making it the simplest element in the universe.

- Speaking of the universe: all hydrogen atoms were created during the birth of the universe. This means that every hydrogen atom in your body is likely billions of years old!

- Coming into contact with radioactivity is known to be incredibly dangerous, but did you know that the bananas you eat as a snack are considered to be slightly radioactive? Unbelievable as it might seem, this is due to them containing a very small amount of an isotope called potassium-40.

- It's incredibly difficult to put out a magnesium fire. If you try to put it out using water, this will produce hydrogen, only intensifying the flames. A normal carbon dioxide fire extinguisher can't be used, because magnesium can still burn in pure nitrogen and pure carbon dioxide! In fact, the only way to put out this kind of fire is to use a chemical fire extinguisher or to cover the fire with sand.

- Lead used to be commonly used in face whitening make-up and to paint children's toys. Thankfully, these practices were stopped in most countries when the highly toxic properties of lead were discovered!

- The boiling point of water changes at different altitudes. At sea level, water boils at 100°C. But if you were to heat a pot of water on top of Mount Everest, for example, it would boil at just 70°C! Can you boil water at lower temperatures? Continue reading to find out!

- Did you know that you can die from drinking too much water? Staying well hydrated is essential for all life, but drinking too much water, about 4 litres within the space of an hour, causes the sodium levels in your body to drop rapidly and allows water to enter the brain. This can cause brain swelling and lead to seizures, trouble breathing and, ultimately, death.

- Mercury is the only metal that remains a liquid at room temperature.
- Corrosion is a destructive process where metals react with their environment. Titanium is not only highly resistant to any form of corrosion, including from seawater and chlorine, but it is the strongest of all metals in relation to its weight. It is, in fact, as strong as steel, even though it is 45% lighter!
- Nickel was once commonly used to make coins, but we made a switch to using cheaper metals when it was discovered that many people find nickel irritating on their skin.
- Dry ice never becomes a liquid. This pretty cool substance is actually solidified carbon dioxide – yes, the stuff you exhale! When you heat it up, instead of becoming a liquid, dry ice immediately becomes a gas (this is a process called sublimation).

- That beautiful, expensive glass vase your mum won't let you touch may look like a solid, but it's actually not! That's right – in its purest form, glass is an amorphous substance, meaning that it's somewhere between a solid and a liquid.

- All flames are dangerous to touch, but did you know that the colour of a flame can actually tell you how hot it is? If a flame is red, you'll know it's between 600 and 800°C. Orange flames are a bit hotter, between 800 and 1,200°C. Blue flames are the hottest of all – they can reach 1,650°C!

- Besides hydrogen and helium, all the elements in our universe were created inside stars through a process known as nuclear fusion.

- Baking is a form of chemistry. Baking bread involves many chemical reactions. One of them is when yeast turns sugars into carbon dioxide, which makes the bread expand. A reaction known as the Maillard reaction also occurs, which makes the bread turn golden brown and tasty!

➡ Modern chemistry has its roots in ancient alchemy, which combined practical knowledge with a philosophical approach to nature and all matter. Alchemists mostly aimed to turn common metals, like lead and copper, into gold, but this goal was never achieved. However, important discoveries about the elements and their capabilities were made in the process.

➡ Ever wondered why some doorknobs and handrails in public buildings are made of copper or brass? This is actually a hygiene precaution – you see, copper is a natural antibacterial! This element has also been used to line parts of ships for centuries so that barnacles and mussels do not stick to the bottom.

➡ Helium balloons float because helium is less dense than air. This means that a balloon filled with helium will be lighter than the same balloon filled with the same volume of air, causing it to float upwards.

➡ Helium has a lifting force of roughly 1 gram per litre. That means a balloon containing 10 litres of helium can only lift an object weighing 10 grams off the ground. Sadly, that also means that if you ever want to be whisked away by a bunch of balloons, you'll need at least 2,000 helium-filled balloons to lift you, if you weigh 20 kilograms!

- Water gets bigger when it freezes, which makes it different from many other substances. This is because of something called hydrogen bonding. The hydrogen atoms in water molecules are polar, so they don't like to be near each other, and make the water expand as it solidifies! An ice cube takes up about 9% more space than it would in its liquid state.

- If you mix together ½ litre of alcohol and ½ litre of water, the resulting liquid will be less than 1 litre in volume. But how is this possible? Well, when you mix water and alcohol, they form hydrogen bonds with each other, and the alcohol molecules slip into spaces between water molecules. You can see this visually if you add water to a full box of pebbles. While the box of pebbles was full in the first place, you manage to add more to it.

BREATHE IN!

- About 28% of the world's oxygen is produced by rainforests. Tiny organisms called planktons that float in our oceans are, however, the largest contributor: they produce at least half of all the oxygen on Earth.

- While oxygen is necessary for a fire to occur, as it supports combustion, it cannot burn on its own and is not inherently a flammable element.

- Oxygen is a gas at room temperature under usual conditions, but it can actually melt and boil, too! This element melts at -218.79°C and boils at -182.95°C.

- While oxygen might appear not to have any colour as a gas, it actually turns a pale blue when it becomes liquid or solid. This is because the pressure forces the molecules closer together, making their true colour clearer to the naked eye.

- Oxygen is the most commonly found element on Earth, making up large quantities of our oceans, atmosphere and Earth's crust.

- There are several forms of oxygen. The type we inhale is actually two oxygen atoms bonded together (O_2). O_3, on the other hand, is three oxygen atoms bonded together, known as ozone. This is not safe to breathe.

- Did you know that oxygen dissolves in water? There is actually oxygen in both fresh water and seawater! Fresh water contains roughly 6.04 ml of oxygen per litre, while seawater contains 4.95 ml of oxygen per litre.

- We need oxygen to survive, but it is possible to have too much of it! Breathing in too much oxygen causes a condition known as the bends, and it's actually something astronauts and scuba divers need to be very wary of. When these individuals inhale too much oxygen too quickly, tiny bubbles can form in their blood, and this can be fatal.

- Did you know your body naturally contains a large amount of carbon? Carbon in its purest form occurs as graphite. Fascinatingly, our bodies contain enough carbon to provide graphite for the creation of 9,000 pencils!

- Ever wondered how tiny an atom is? To give you an idea, one bucket filled with water contains more atoms than there are buckets of water in the Atlantic Ocean!

- While both are equally painful, bee stings and wasp stings are quite different due to the pH of the venom in each sting. Bee venom is acidic, which is why rubbing an alkaline substance, such as baking soda, on it may help to relieve the effects. The pH of wasp venom is alkaline, but only by a narrow margin.

- The molecule capsaicin is what makes hot peppers spicy and irritating to the tongue. Mammals react to this molecule, but birds don't have the receptor needed to experience it, meaning they can consume hot peppers without feeling a thing!

- The planet Mars appears red because its surface comprises large amounts of iron oxide, known more commonly to us as rust. The atmosphere on the planet contains both water and carbon dioxide, which provide oxygen for the iron to react with, resulting in its vibrant red colour.

- The periodic table was invented by Dmitri Mendeleev in 1869, in an attempt to arrange all the elements systematically. While other scientists had tried to make tables such as this in the past, Mendeleev's is the most widely approved among the scientific community.

- The periodic table is constantly under review and subject to updates and improvements. When Dmitri Mendeleev first presented it, it only included 63 elements. Whereas today, we have 118 elements in the table – and counting!

- In 2016, the newest elements were added to the periodic table. Research groups from Japan, the US and Russia discovered elements numbered 113, 115, 117 and 118, and three of them were named after the places in which they were discovered: nihonium, moscovium and tennessine. The fourth was named after a nuclear physicist, oganesson.

- Around 95 of the 118 elements on the periodic table are metals. Some elements are more difficult to classify, however, because the distinctions between metals, nonmetals and metalloids are not globally agreed upon.

- The elements found in the periodic table are what make up matter all across the universe. This means that the elements found on Mars or in another galaxy are the same elements that make up the matter on Earth.

- The only letter in the alphabet that does not appear on the periodic table is J.

- Many of the elements on the periodic table occur naturally, but there are a few that are man-made. The first ever man-made element, technetium, was discovered in 1937 in Italy and was found to be present in spent nuclear fuel rods.

➡ A famous chemist, Glenn Seaborg, is the only person who could ever write their full address using only elements on the periodic table. The address was: Sg (seaborgium – the element named after Seaborg himself), Lr (lawrencium – the element named after the Lawrence Berkeley National Laboratory), Bk (berkelium – an element named after Berkeley, the city), Cf (californium – named after California), Am (americium – named after the US).

➡ The magnificent fireworks show that lights up the sky on New Year's Eve is nothing but a display of chemical reactions. Copper gives off a blue colour, sodium gives off yellow, barium gives off green and strontium gives off red.

➡ The gold medals awarded at the Olympic Games actually only contain about 6 grams of gold and are mostly made of silver.

➡ Gold is a pretty malleable element – just 1 gram can be hammered down into a thin sheet reaching 1 square metre in size! It can also be made so thin that it looks transparent.

➡ Did you know our kitchens are like science labs, full of colour-changing magic? The juices of many foods we eat, like blueberries, red cabbage, red onion or spices like turmeric, can change colour when mixed with things like lemon juice (which is acidic) or baking soda (which is alkaline). These foods can transform from their usual colours into a whole different spectrum, turning cooking into an exciting science experiment!

ACTIVITY: FIND YOUR (PH) BALANCE

With your newfound knowledge about chemistry and the elements found in the periodic table, you are ready to explore chemistry hands-on! Carry out this experiment at home with family or friends using food ingredients found in your kitchen and watch the magic of pH unfold before your very eyes.

The pH scale is used to identify how acidic or alkaline a liquid is; pH indicators change colour depending on the pH of the solution they are in.

There are several ingredients that you can use to create your own pH indicators at home. All of them are ingredients you'd typically find in the kitchen and use for cooking.

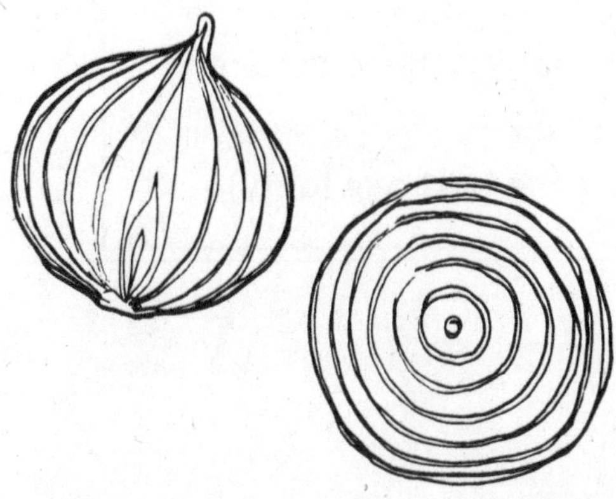

Materials

- Hot water
- A jug that can withstand hot water
- A colander
- Six clear cups or glasses
- Indicator testers. Find any liquid that is safe to handle and you want to test.
- Here are examples:
  - lemon juice
  - distilled vinegar
  - tap water
  - fizzy water
  - handwash
  - baking soda
  - washing powder or liquid
- One food pH indicator from the list below

Check what pH indicator you have at home to start straight away:

- Red cabbage (it is the best one to try)

- Red onion (make sure to use the inner-most layers of the onion, not the dry outer layers)
- Turmeric (add the spice to water and stir well to get a yellow-orange liquid)
- Blueberries, blackberries or cranberries (squish the berries and add water to get your indicator liquid)
- Hibiscus tea

If you do not have any of these at the moment, you can try making a cup of black tea and see how its colour changes when you add a piece of lemon.

Instructions

1. Firstly, you need to get juice from the food you chose to use as a pH indicator. Place pieces of it in a jug (leaves from red cabbage, cut onions or squashed berries) and add boiling water. Allow this mixture to cool for a while. When it is cool enough to handle, use a colander to separate the liquid from everything else.

The more saturated the colour is, the better you will see the colour change (but not too dark).

2. Next, place your clear cups in a row, equal distance from one another, and pour equal amounts of the liquid you made into each cup.
3. Now, it's time to prepare your testers. You can have some lemon juice, distilled vinegar, some fizzy water, a small amount of washing-up liquid, some washing powder or liquid, and a small amount of baking soda.
4. Let's make the magic happen! Carefully pour a small amount of each tester into a clear cup containing your pH indicator. Observe as a colour change occurs in each cup, and write down how the liquid reacts to each tester. Which testers bring about the greatest colour change? Which testers cause little to no change in colour?

Take it further

Arrange all the cups in order from most acidic on the left to most alkaline on the right based on their colour.

Here is a general guide for interpreting the colour changes if you use Red Cabbage as an indicator: red (highly acidic), pink (moderately acidic), no colour change (neutral), blue (slightly alkaline), green (moderately alkaline), yellow (highly alkaline).

Other pH indicators from our list might show different colours, try them to find out.

OUT OF THIS WORLD

Space, **Physics** and golf on the moon

- Did you know that it's possible to freeze and boil water at the same time? It sounds unfathomable, but if you were to reduce the air pressure and temperature, this unthinkable feat of physics could be achieved! This is called 'triple point' and for water it occurs at a temperature of 0.01°C and a pressure of 0.006 atm (611.73 Pa).

- Trees on Earth outnumber stars in our galaxy! That's right; there are approximately 3 trillion trees on planet Earth and only an estimated 300 billion stars in the Milky Way!

- Ever wished you could time travel? Well, flying aboard an aeroplane is probably as close as you can get today! Einstein stated, with his theory of relativity, that moving objects experience the effects of time more slowly than stationary objects. An experiment performed in 1971, known as the Hafele-Keating experiment, proved this by showing that atomic clocks on board aeroplanes lagged slightly when compared to atomic clocks in one fixed location.

- People in different cultures tend to have varying ideas about how time works. For example, in the

Western world, we picture time as linear, and if we were to draw a timeline, we would draw it from left to right. However, people who speak languages that are written in the opposite direction will picture time as moving from right to left. A tribe of people living in the Andes Mountains known as the Aymara think of the future as being behind them, with the past laid out in front of them. Some choose to use directions like north, south, east and west to describe time too!

- In the year 46 BC, Julius Caesar decided to change the calendar to the 365-day year one we use today. In order to get the calendar in sync, he ordered there to be a 445-day-long year to catch up with the seasons – the longest calendar year in our recorded history!

- Mercury is the fastest planet in our solar system, making its way around the sun in only 88 days. It shoots across its orbit at almost 47 kilometres per second, compared to Earth's 30 kilometres per second or 107,000 kilometres per hour, as you learnt at the start of our quest!

- On the planet Venus, one day is longer than one year! This is due to the fact that this planet turns incredibly slowly on its axis, and takes a total of 243 Earth days to make a full turn. This means that a day on Venus is equal to 243 days on Earth. However, it takes only 225 Earth days to orbit the sun, so a year on Venus is 18 Earth days shorter than one day on Venus!

- The mass of the Sun takes up 99.86% of our solar system.

- Musical instruments can't make any sound in outer space. That's because space has no atmosphere, which means the sound has no way of being transmitted. Even when pieces of space debris crash into each other, or stars explode, it makes absolutely no noise!

- Did you know that golf is the only sport that has been played on the moon? The commander of the Apollo 14 mission, Alan Shepard, famously hit a couple of golf balls using a Wilson six-iron head attached to a lunar sample scoop handle in 1971! However, aboard the International Space Station, astronauts had the opportunity to take part in other sports too, like playing zero-gravity football and basketball. As you can guess, they had to modify the rules of those games to adjust them to the absence of gravity.

- We know that the Sun is unbelievably hot, but the Earth's core is as hot as the Sun's surface! Way down there, temperatures can soar all the way to 5,500°C.

- All of the planets in our solar system, and nearly all the asteroids, orbit around the sun in the same direction. This direction would be considered anticlockwise, if you were to stand way above the Earth's North Pole and look out into space.

- While it may look like they do, several planets don't have a solid surface that humans could walk upon. Jupiter, Saturn, Neptune and Uranus – known as the Jovian planets – are made up mostly of helium and hydrogen and therefore don't have solid surfaces like Earth and Mars. They're basically giant balls of gas!

- If something huge were to smash into our planet, it could alter our orbital trajectory, but the impact made by such an event would likely destroy the Earth altogether.

- Think Mount Everest was high? An asteroid in space called Vesta has a mountain reaching 22 kilometres in height, making it the tallest mountain known to humankind!

- Want to see how wavelengths work? Hold one end of a rope, while your friend holds the other. Move one end of it slowly from side to side, and you'll see a demonstration of how long wavelengths work. For short wavelengths, wiggle your end of the rope rapidly.

- Did you know that it rains on other planets, too? However, it's often quite different to the rain we experience on Earth. For example, Venus experiences drops of sulphuric acid falling to its surface instead of water droplets, and the heat on this planet is so intense that the droplets evaporate before they even land!

- Every comet is as old as our solar system itself. These masses made of sand, ice and carbon dioxide are simply leftovers from when our solar system came into being 4.5 billion years ago. Most of them, if frozen, would be the size of a whole town!

- Clouds may look light and fluffy, but all that water retention actually makes them incredibly heavy. The average cloud can weigh 500,000 kilograms!

- Lightning bolts exude an immense amount of energy. In fact, one single bolt of lightning can contain the amount of energy required to power a 25-watt light bulb for over a year!

- Nothing in the universe can travel faster than the speed of light. It moves at about 1 billion kilometres per hour, while the speed of sound is only 1,235 kilometres per hour! That's why you see lightning much sooner than you hear thunder, even though the sight and sound come from the same source.

- Did you know that thunder is the effect of a shockwave? Whenever a lightning bolt strikes, air rapidly expands and contracts, creating a shock-wave that ripples through the sky and creates that thunderous boom!

- There are 1,800 thunderstorms happening at the same time on Earth at any given moment. This amounts to 16 million storms every year.

- Halley's Comet is one of the most well-known comets, named after the astronomer and mathematician Edmond Halley. It comes into our solar system only once every 75 years, and it was last visible from Earth in 1986. That means we won't see it again until 2061 – how old will you be when that happens?

- It may sound impossible but, in theory, a Formula 1 race car could drive upside down in a tunnel at 200 km/h! The immense downforce that is produced by this particular vehicle's aerodynamic design would help it to stick to the ceiling and keep driving forward.

- While Celsius and Fahrenheit are two very different measures of temperature, they converge at the value of -40. Yes, -40 degrees Celsius is the same as -40 degrees Fahrenheit!

- Not all planets in our solar system rotate in the same way Earth does. Venus rotates in the opposite direction to Earth. While we turn anticlockwise, Venus turns clockwise! Uranus is the only planet in our solar system that rotates on its side.

- Did you know that galaxies are constantly moving? The closest galaxy to ours, the Andromeda Galaxy, is expected to collide with our own in 3.75 billion years. They will then form a giant elliptical (smooth, oval-shaped) galaxy.

- The largest water discovery ever made was a massive cloud of water vapour located 10 billion light years away from Earth, which appears to hold 140 trillion times more water than all our oceans put together!

- Up until 2006, our solar system consisted of nine planets. However, this dropped to eight when the International Astronomical Union made its definitions of a planet more strict, deciding to effectively demote Pluto to a dwarf planet.

➡ All planets in our solar system, except Earth and Uranus, are named after Roman gods and goddesses. Uranus is named after the Greek god of the sky. Earth, however, is an Old English/ Germanic word that means 'ground'.

➡ Over a billion years ago, a day on Earth was only about 18 hours long. This was because, back then, the moon was further away than it is today. Now, days are longer because gravity from the moon has caused the rotation of the Earth to slow down, adding more hours of daylight to our lives. Continue reading to learn how many days dinosaurs were waiting to celebrate the New Year!

➡ We've heard of black holes, but did you know there are white holes, too? White holes are theoretical objects that spew out matter instead of sucking it in, the way black holes do. While we like to theorise about their existence, we've never actually seen one, and don't expect to find one in our universe.

- In a surprising feat of physics, a crumpled piece of paper is actually stronger than a flattened piece of paper. The creases in the paper absorb force, and evenly distribute it across the surface, adding to its strength!

- Is teleportation possible? Scientists have found a way to teleport very small singular particles on a subatomic level in recent years, using something called quantum entanglement. This technology, however, is a very far way away from reaching a point where it could teleport humans!

- Because stars and space matter are so far away from us here on Earth, looking up at the night sky is like looking back into the past. The light we see from stars took a very long time to reach us, so when we look at them, we see what they looked like years ago.

- While the moon has large craters to show evidence of its many collisions with asteroids, meteors and space debris during its existence, the Earth has also had its fair share of collisions. However, on Earth, we have tsunamis, soil erosion, volcanic eruptions, earthquakes and other natural disasters that slowly erode all evidence of our impacts with space matter. Because the moon has no atmosphere, none of these events can occur, leaving it spotted with large craters!

- While we all aim to make our mark in life, anyone who has been on the moon has left it in a very literal sense. Because there is no wind on the moon, there has been no disturbance to the footprints and rover tyre tracks left there since our last visit. In fact, it's believed that those marks will remain on the moon for millions of years to come.
- The largest moon in our solar system belongs to Jupiter, and its name is Ganymede. It's bigger than Mercury and Pluto!
- Saturn is the only planet in our solar system that is less dense than water. That means if you put it in a (very, very large) bathtub, it would float!
- Theoretically, astronauts could propel themselves through space by exhaling! Breathing out would

propel them in the opposite direction, similarly to how air escaping from a balloon would propel a balloon car!

ACTIVITY: START YOUR ENGINES

Now that you've gained so much valuable information about space and physics, actual events happening around you might start to make a lot more sense. For example, a car's engine is quite complicated, and whether it works or not depends on many factors that are meticulously and perfectly calculated, but did you know that there are a lot of simple, physics-based ways you can make toy cars move all on their own? That's right! In this simple activity that you can perform at home, I'll show you how . . .

Materials

- A balloon
- A paper straw
- Some tape or rubber band
- A toy car (you can build one using LEGO bricks or other materials)
- Lots of lung capacity!

Instructions

1. Insert the paper straw into the open hole of the balloon and secure it with tape. Then, place the length of the straw on the body of your toy car, with the balloon on the front end, and use several pieces of tape to secure it.
2. Blow into the straw until the balloon is inflated and pinch the balloon so the air stays inside.
3. Now put the car on the floor or table, release the balloon and watch your little car zoot around, powered by the air!
4. Think about what changes you can make so your car goes further. Adding a bigger balloon or two? Making the car heavier or lighter?

Take it further

You can explore other ways to move your car! Attach one magnet to your toy car, and hold the other magnet in your hand. Move magnets closer and, depending on the polarisation of the magnets, they will repel or attract and move the car at the same time.

Try finding other ways you can propel your toy car forward. Whether you will be using rubber bands or attaching sails to your car, I hope you will enjoy exploring physics!

TECTONIC TWISTERS

Geoscience, culture
and the rock we call home

- Although roughly 71% of the Earth's surface is covered with water, all the water on Earth by volume makes up just 0.02% of the planet.

- The amount of water that exists on Earth has never changed. Today, we have the same amount of water that was present on our planet millions of years ago, when dinosaurs were around.

- NWA 11119 is the oldest meteorite formed from cooled magma or lava that we've found on our planet. It is estimated to be roughly 4.6 billion years old. That's older than the Earth itself, and almost as old as our solar system! The 'NWA' in its name refers to where it was found – Northwest Africa – and '11119' is the identification number it has been assigned.

- Did you know that you'll always be seven years ahead of Ethiopia? Fascinatingly, the Ethiopians live on an entirely different calendar, setting them back approximately seven years. While the rest of the world uses the Gregorian calendar, this African country calculates the start of their year differently, which also leads them to celebrate New Year on 11 September and Christmas on 7 January.

- Adopted in 1981, Belize's national flag has more colours than any other national flag in the world. The 12 colours depict the country's coat of arms on a blue background, with red stripes along the top and bottom of the flag. It was adopted after the nation gained its independence from the United Kingdom.

- Ever tried to guess what's hidden beneath the wrapping paper of your Christmas present before opening it? Well, this is kind of how we've guessed what's below the surface of the Earth! You see, when we talk about the Earth's crust, mantle and core, this is actually just a working theory. Known as the 'layered Earth theory', this calculated estimation states that the crust is the part of the Earth that we exist upon, the outermost layer, while the mantle is a much hotter layer that lies underneath and the core is located at the very centre of the planet. However, because we've never been able to dig that deep into the Earth's surface, we have only a theory as to what lies down there. It could be completely different!

➡ All the Earth's continents were once joined as one supercontinent called Pangaea. The Earth's crust is split into several large tectonic plates and, about 335 million years ago, these plates were joined together to form Pangaea. However, because these tectonic plates are always moving, the massive land mass ultimately split apart about 175 million years ago to form the different continents we have today. One day, scientists predict that the movement of the tectonic plates may once again form another giant continent, which will be called Pangaea Proxima.

➡ Iceland is growing by nearly 5 centimetres every year. It happens because it sits right where the North American and Eurasian tectonic plates meet and as these plates move apart, the land splits and magma rises to the surface, resulting in volcanic activity and the formation of new crust.

- Plastiglomerate is a newly discovered kind of rock that is formed from plastic waste, sediment, shells and debris. The first samples of this rock were found in Hawaii in 2006, and the discovery is a clear indication of how plastic pollution affects our natural environment.

- The Atacama Desert is one of the driest places on Earth, where no rain has fallen for hundreds of years. Despite this, certain species of bacteria and fungi have still been able to survive there.

- A valley named Oymyakon in Yakutia is the coldest inhabited place on Earth. Also known as the Pole of Cold, this valley has temperatures that drop as low as -70°C! While these conditions may seem unlivable, a small community of about 500 Siberian people herd, hunt and fish in this region.

- Ōkunoshima is an island in Japan where the only permanent residents are rabbits!

- Hang Son Doong is the world's largest natural cave, located in Vietnam. There is a subterranean river there and it is so vast that it even has its own localised weather system. Clouds can form inside these massive hollows and it can rain inside the cave!

- South America, the location of the Amazon Rainforest, is often incorrectly thought of as the most forested area in the world. In actual fact, Russia is the most forested country in the world, with its Boreal Forest region boasting an impressive 815 million hectares of forest!

- Did you know that Bangkok, the capital of Thailand, has another name? In fact, it's the longest name of any city in the world! Formerly known as Krung Thep Mahanakhon Amon Rattanakosin Mahinthara Ayuthaya Mahadilok Phop Noppharat Ratchathani Burirom Udomratchaniwet Mahasathan Amon Piman Awatan Sathit Sakkathattiya Witsanukam Prasit, the city chose to settle instead for the shorter and more convenient 'Bangkok' in place of its 21-word name. Imagine writing that address on a postcard!

- We all have dream destinations, but it seems that many people – approximately 90 million every year – all have this exact thought about France. Indeed, it's the most-visited country in the world, tailed closely by Spain and the United States.

- Think the walk from your bedroom to the kitchen is long? Maybe don't visit the Great Wall of China anytime soon. At a mind-boggling 21,196 kilometres long, it would take you about 6 months to walk along its entire length if you walk nonstop without any breaks. It was originally built during the third century BC as a means to protect China's territory from invaders, and it took over 2,000 years to fully construct it!

- Zealandia, a massive sunken continent, was submerged after breaking away from Australia approximately 60–85 million years ago. New Zealand and New Caledonia are the only parts of Zealandia that stay above water, but a staggering 94% of it is underwater.

- Because the Sahara Desert is known to get little rain, you'd never imagine that this part of the world would be capable of experiencing snowfall. However, this seeming impossibility became real in 2018, and for just one day, the hot sand was covered in glistening white snow! It quickly melted under the baking-hot sun.

- Sand dunes in the Sahara Desert can reach a height of 180 metres – roughly twice the height of Big Ben in London!

- Today, we know the Sahara Desert as the world's largest hot desert, spanning over 9.2 million square kilometres. But did you know that it used to be a tropical rainforest? That's right – only 6,000 years ago, this barren land was a lush rainforest with thick vegetation, a tropical climate and lots of rain!

- Point Nemo is a place in the ocean that is the farthest away from any land. If you were to go here, you'd be closer to the astronauts in space than to any people living on Earth! The International Space Station orbits the Earth from approximately 408 kilometres away, while the closest land dwellers to Point Nemo are over 2,600 kilometres away!

- Places closer to the equator are subject to slightly weaker gravity. It's easy to assume that the pull of gravity would be equally strong everywhere on Earth, but the centrifugal force from the rotation of the Earth is at its strongest near the equator, interfering with the strength of gravity.

LINGUISTIC LABYRINTHS

- The world is a vast, diverse and fascinating place, and it is our human differences that make life on Earth so interesting. There are over 7,000 languages spoken across the globe. Mandarin Chinese, Spanish, English and Hindi are the languages with the highest number of speakers, and some very rare languages only have one or two living speakers! While it may have many speakers, Mandarin Chinese is widely considered the most difficult language to learn.

- The Turkish village of Kuşköy still uses an incredibly rare, whistling language known as 'bird language' in a centuries-old tradition that has now been listed on the UNESCO list of Intangible Cultural Heritage. While the language isn't used to communicate with birds, the sounds have been said to mimic bird calls. These high-pitched noises were specifically chosen to carry over the region's steep mountain ranges and across long distances.

- Of all the languages in the world, the Bible has been translated into 3,384 of them, making it the most widely translated book available. (But Agatha Christie takes the title of the world's most widely translated author.)

- As far as alphabets go, the English alphabet – with 26 letters – is pretty average. In comparison, the language with the longest alphabet in the world is the Cambodian language Khmer, clocking in an impressive 74 letters. Rotokas, spoken in a small part of Papua New Guinea, has the shortest alphabet in the world with only 12 letters.

- There are over 200 artificial languages that have been constructed for movies, television and books. Thirteen of these belong to the Tolkien universe.

- While many countries have populations that speak a number of languages, Bolivia has the most official languages of any country, totalling 37. This is due to Bolivia being home to a multicultural and multi-ethnic population, with a high number of indigenous communities, each having their own language.

➡ Ever heard of an island within a lake, on an island within a lake, on an island? This rare phenomenon is called a 'third-order' island. There is one in the Philippines and it is called Vulcan Point. To break it down, the small rocky island of Vulcan Point is located on the Main Crater Lake of Taal Volcano, which is situated on the larger Taal Island, which is an island in Lake Taal. Lake Taal itself is located on the Philippine island of Luzon.

- Vatican City is the world's smallest country by land area. This tiny country is located entirely within the city of Rome in Italy.

- One of the most powerful volcanic eruptions in recorded history caused a 'year without summer' due to its release of enormous amounts of sulphur dioxide and ash into the Earth's atmosphere. This eruption of the Indonesian volcano Tambora took place in 1815, and its effects impacted global weather patterns. The temperature dropped around the world and many harvests failed, resulting in a global food shortage. Volcanoes can erupt in several different ways: effusive eruptions happen when lava flows like a river, while explosive eruptions blast out ash and rocks over 20 kilometres through the air. You can witness your very own at-home volcanic eruption using lemons, soap and baking soda by reading on!

ACTIVITY: UNLEASH THE POWER OF CITRUS!

I'm sure you're reeling after finding out so many riveting facts about the world we live in. Before you run off to share all this new information with anyone who will listen, it's time to watch natural wonders unfurl before your eyes in your very own home! In this easy yet engaging task, you'll get to see the magic that happens when you combine everyday ingredients lying around in your kitchen. You know what they say: when life gives you lemons . . . watch them erupt!

Materials

- A lemon
- A large glass dish
- Food colouring
- Baking soda
- Liquid hand soap/washing-up liquid
- A knife
- A spoon

Instructions

1. Start by cutting off the two ends of the lemon and then cut it in half, leaving you with two equally sized lemon halves that have flat bottoms to stay put.
2. Place the lemon halves, with the wider part facing upwards, inside the large glass dish. The dish ensures that we don't make a mess all over the kitchen worktop when our lemons start fizzing over with 'lava', and makes our cleaning-up process a lot easier!
3. Pour a few drops of food colouring and a small amount of liquid hand soap onto the exposed surface of each lemon half.
4. Place a teaspoon of baking soda on top of the lemon halves. And now . . . watch in amazement! Your lemon halves will erupt, like small acidic volcanoes, into fizzy explosions of vibrant colours. To make the reaction bigger, use a spoon to push baking soda inside the lemons.

So, what causes this marvellous explosion? When the baking soda reacts with the acidic lemon juice, carbon dioxide is released from the lemon. The hand soap catches the carbon dioxide in bubbles! And just like that, you have two small bubbly lemon volcanoes fizzing away right in front of your eyes!

CAREFUL, THE ROBOT MAY BYTE

Engineering, Technology
and flying cars

- The first cars did not have a steering wheel. Drivers were changing directions with the help of a lever for almost a decade until the handy steering wheel was invented in 1894!

- The fastest camera ever invented can capture as many as 10 trillion frames per second. This incredible feat of modern technology allows us to observe phenomena that are unbelievably fast, such as the movement of light!

- A bionic eye has been developed that surpasses the capability of human vision. This device allows us to see ultraviolet and infrared light, as well as visualise the polarisation of light.

- Constructing buildings is difficult enough on Earth, so you can only imagine the challenges involved with building in space! The International Space Station was constructed over 10 years, and took more than 30 missions into space to complete.

- Did you know that Google rents a herd of goats in place of lawnmowers? That's right – at their Mountain View headquarters in 2009, Google opted to rent 200 goats to eat the grass in place of mowing the lawns. It turned out to be such a good idea that nowadays you can easily find a goat to rent for gardening too. No, I'm not kidding!

- Invented in the twelfth century, the compass is a reliable piece of tech because it uses a magnetic field that runs between the North and South poles of our Earth to guide us. This also means that a compass will continue to work if you go underground – the magnetic field is just as strong beneath the depths of the ocean, or at the bottom of a mineshaft! However, because this magnetic field is maintained by the swirling molten iron at the core of our planet, you'd find that your compass would go crazy if you were ever able to dig that deep!

- Bad aeroplane food is the least of our worries – imagine being struck by lightning all the way up in the air! The US National Weather Service reports that commercial aircraft are hit by lightning bolts once or twice every year on average. Luckily, advances in modern technology have ensured that it isn't hugely damaging to the planes we travel in. In fact, no plane has crashed due to a lightning bolt hitting it since 1967.

- Companies like Tesla perpetuate the belief that electric cars are a new and revolutionary invention. In reality, they were originally developed all the way back in the 1830s, before gasoline-powered cars! One of the reasons they are making such a popular comeback today is because of climate-related concerns.

- The engines of electric cars are not only more environmentally friendly, they're also much simpler! An electric engine contains roughly 20 moving parts, while a much more complicated gasoline engine has over 2,000!

- Apple is known today as one of the most successful tech companies in the world. But did you know that it was also the first ever public company to achieve a value of 3 trillion US dollars?

- The Danyang-Kunshan Grand Bridge, located in China and finished in 2011 after four years of construction, is the longest bridge in the world.

Its total length measures over 160 kilometres, and it cost roughly 8.5 billion US dollars to build!

- An innovatively designed robot named Atlas has such diverse mobility that it can even do a back-flip! The humanoid creation belongs to Boston Dynamics and aims to push the boundaries of robotic engineering, with its impressive parkour and gymnastic abilities constantly improving.

- Flying cars are a feat of engineering often seen in futuristic sci-fi movies, but it may surprise you to learn that engineers have actually accomplished this seemingly impossible milestone. The AirCar is one such prototype that is currently in development, created in 2017 by Klein Vision. This astonishing invention transforms from a fully functional motor vehicle to an aircraft in 2 minutes and 15 seconds!

- While we consider the computer a relatively recent invention, the very first analogue computer was actually created 2,000 years ago! The Antikythera Mechanism was a hand-powered device that helped ancient Greek civilisations to predict the movements of stars and planets. However, the rapid advancement of digital computers is something that has only sped up in the last 20 years or so, ultimately leading us to the highly technical and fast-paced computers we use today.

- The tallest building in the world, the Burj Khalifa, is located in Dubai. It towers 828 metres into the air, and this astonishing height is achieved through its unique design – it twists slightly as it goes higher, breaking up the wind at high altitudes so that it doesn't sway.

- The fastest recorded speed that a car has ever travelled at is 1,227.985 kilometres per hour (763.035 mph), a record set by the first vehicle to ever break the sound barrier! This speed was achieved back in 1997 by a jet-powered vehicle driven by Andy Green.

- The greatest depth a person has ever travelled to was reached after 4 hours of diving below surface level into the Challenger Deep – the deepest known section of the ocean. This record-breaking depth was 10,935 metres. Unbelievably, plastic litter has been found at these momentous depths!

- The fastest supercomputer in the world is used by the US Department of Energy to perform scientific research. Frontier conducts more than 1.1 quintillion calculations every second! If every human in the world solved one maths problem every second, it would still take us 4 years to complete the same amount of work that Frontier can produce in 1 second.

- Hailed as a marvel of geometry, engineering and biomechanics, the snowboard may seem like an ordinary object, but the specifics of this invention are actually highly calculated. It was invented by an engineer, Sherman Poppen, in 1965. The design has evolved significantly over time, allowing snowboarders to perform more impressive tricks and become more aerodynamic.

- You may know the Ferris wheel as a fun theme park ride or the provider of great views, but this invention is actually a wonder of the engineering world. It was first created by George W. Ferris in 1893. The wheel of the mechanism is supported by high steel towers and connected by a long, strong axle. The tallest one, the Ain Dubai, is located in Dubai and stands at 250 metres!

- The Eiffel Tower shrinks and grows depending on the temperature. Because it's made of iron, its height increases in hot weather when the iron expands, causing it to grow up to 15 centimetres taller than it usually would be during the winter!

- One of the largest mosques in the world, the Sheikh Zayed Grand Mosque, is located in Abu Dhabi. It is supported by over 1,000 pillars and has an incredibly luxurious interior. What may surprise you is that the most expensive part of this architectural marvel is the enormous carpet: it is, in fact, the largest hand-woven carpet in the world! 38 tons of wool and cotton were used in its creation, and it measures 5,627 square metres.

- The most iconic statue in the United States was a gift from France. While it has become a significant visual symbol of freedom, the Statue of Liberty, located in New York City, was given to the US by its ally France in 1886, and comes in at an impressive 93 metres tall.

- Seeing a swaying building might ring alarm bells for some, but in the case of the CN Tower in Toronto, Canada, it's perfectly normal for this structure to sway up to half a metre in high winds. It also gets struck by lightning about 75 times every year!

- Beneath the streets of Cincinnati in the US lies an abandoned structure of tunnels and stations that have never been used. While this was approved for construction in the early 1900s to upgrade the streetcar system, it was interrupted by the First World War and eventually abandoned due to inflating prices and political obstructions. However, it still lies there today!

- Now synonymous with any artificial human likeness, the word 'robot' actually has a pretty dark hidden meaning. The word originally comes from the Czech word *'robota'*, which means forced labour or work. First used during a play in the 1920s, the term simply stuck!

- While reading from screens has undoubtedly become more popular, you might not want to give up your paperbacks just yet . . . Research has found that, on average, people read 10% slower from a screen than from paper! You also blink much less frequently when reading from a screen, which may cause your eyes to become dry and strained. So, keep asking for books for Christmas!

➡ The first computer mouse was very different to the ones we use today. Doug Engelbart first stumbled upon this invention in 1964, only, back then, it was made from wood instead of plastic. He named it a 'mouse' because the cord connecting it to the computer reminded him of a mouse's tail.

➡ If it would only wake you up at 4am, would you still want your alarm clock? Well, the very first one did exactly that. Invented in 1787 by Levi Hutchins, it would only sound off once, at 4 in the morning, every day! Luckily, in 1876, the wind-up alarm clock was invented, and the ringer could be set for any time.

➡ Did you know that Nintendo existed long before computers? Founded in 1889, the company sold playing cards before video games were invented.

- Have you ever been convinced you heard your phone buzz, but looked at the screen to see no new messages? This is a symptom of a very real condition called Phantom Vibration Syndrome, and it's when you think your phone is vibrating, but it isn't. Research indicates that this is caused by an over-dependence on cellular phones. So, back to books again!

- Would you ever consider a mobile phone more essential than a toilet? Surprisingly, out of the world's 7.7 billion people, over 6 billion have access to a cell phone, while only 4.5 billion have a toilet at home.

- Some people have a phobia of technology. Named technophobia, this fear has roots all the way back in the Industrial Revolution, when workers feared that new machines would take their jobs.

KNOW YOUR TOYS!

- The very first jigsaw puzzle was created in 1760, when John Spilsbury glued maps of the world onto wood and cut the wood into pieces. It was used to teach young children about geography and help them learn the location of different countries. These puzzles became popular and started selling to elite boarding schools until they became the iconic games they are today.

- When it was first invented, the humble hula hoop took the world by storm. First sold in 1958, its manufacturing company, Wham-O, recorded 25 million sales within its first four months on sale!

- LEGO is one of the most iconic toy brands that exists today. It was founded in 1932 in Denmark, and every person in the world owns an average of 86 LEGO bricks.

- Did you know that there's a word for the study and science of puzzles? Enig-matology explores puzzles of any kind, whether mathematical, word or logic related.

- Call her Barbie for short! Barbie, the most recognisable doll in the world, actually has a full name. Yes, her real name is Barbara Millicent Roberts! The name came from Barbie's original creator, Ruth Handler, who named the doll 'Barbara' after her daughter.

- Your toy yo-yo may seem simple and unassuming, but it has a fascinating history as one of the oldest toys in the world! While its country of origin is undecided, with some saying it originated in China, the Philippines or Greece, there is undeniable evidence of its existence dating back to the year 500 BC.

- The fastest recorded time it took someone to solve a 3x3x3 rotating puzzle cube is 3.13 seconds! This incredible record was set by the speedcubing giant and Guinness World Records Hall of Fame member Max

Park, from the United States. He was only 21 years old!

- The international crayon manufacturing company Crayola churns out nearly 3 billion crayons every year. That's enough crayons to circle our planet 6 times!

- The longest marble run was created on 1 September in Flumserberg, Switzerland, and measured 2,858.9 metres. However, the 1,413.67-metre marble run inside the Universum science facility in Bremen, Germany set a world record for the longest running time, with their marble run of 36 minutes!

ACTIVITY: GET THE BALL ROLLING!

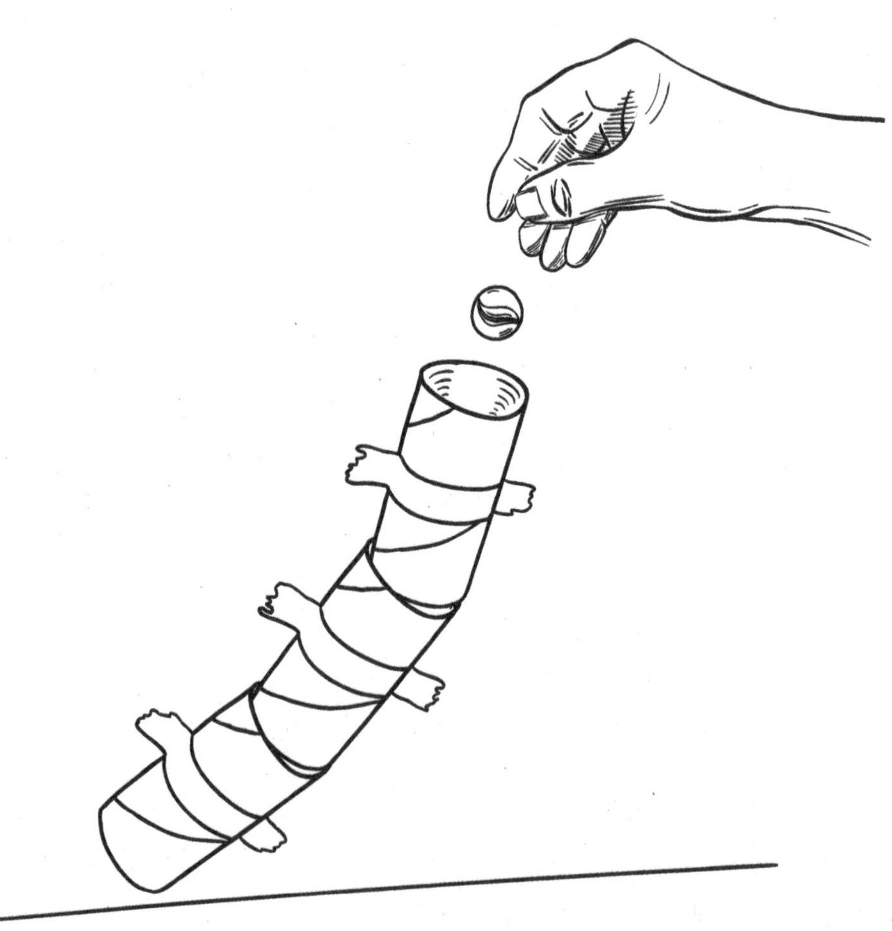

Has the wonderful world of technology and engineering enthralled you? While your brain is surely reeling after absorbing all the info-packed facts, there's still more to come with this fun and challenging at-home activity. Today, you'll be making your very own marble run – a fun-filled activity for the whole family!

Materials

- Masking tape
- Several empty toilet paper or kitchen towel rolls
- Marbles (or small balls or pom-poms)

Instructions

1. Find a clear wall that doesn't have any art in your house and use masking tape to attach the tubes to it. Make sure that each tube is attached securely with multiple pieces of masking tape and that there are no gaps between where one tube ends and another begins. You don't want any of your marbles to fall through!
2. As much as this activity allows you a lot of creative freedom, you'll also need to switch your engineering brain on to make sure that the marble will flow through the tube design easily!
3. Place a box at the end so that the marbles fall directly into it and don't tumble out all over the floor.
4. Once you're confident that your tunnel is securely attached to the wall and has no gaps, it's time to put it to the test! Pour your marbles into the entry point of the tunnel!

Take it further

Experiment with other materials for your marble run! It's fun to use a clear plastic sheet rolled up into a tube shape and attach it between two cardboard tubes. This way, you can see your marbles rolling through your long tunnel at certain points! Try to include some obstacles for the marbles flowing through the run, you can use textured material to make their journey a little bumpier and more dynamic.

THAT NEVER GETS OLD

History, origins and Viking tweezers

- Early humans began in Africa and remained there for their first few million years. It was only about 1.8 million years ago that we began travelling to other parts of the world.

- We are *homo sapiens* – the only surviving species of the genus 'Homo', the scientific name translating to 'wise man' from Latin. It was first coined by Swedish botanist and taxonomist Carl Linnaeus.

- We weren't the only human species to inhabit the Earth! We shared the same geographic areas with at least three other early human species. Only about 70,000 years ago, there were *Denisovans, Homo floresiensis*, and *Homo neanderthalensis*. The last of these – *Homo neanderthalensis*, commonly known today as the Neanderthals – are thought to have interbred with early *Homo sapiens* when the two species encountered one another, and this explains why recent genetic studies have found traces of Neanderthal DNA in most humans today of non-African descent.

- *Homo erectus*, another species of early humans, established itself as one of the longest-surviving human species to ever walk the Earth! Living longer than any other human, including *Homo sapiens*, they are thought to have lived for about 1.8 million years. We've been around for a relatively short time in comparison – only 300,000 years!

- The number of people on Earth has grown astronomically in quite a short space of time. It is estimated that 5 million humans occupied the Earth in 8000 BC – that's only about half the number of people currently living in London, UK!

- Back when dinosaurs walked the Earth, it actually rotated faster than it does today. This made days shorter, which meant they experienced 380 days in a year, instead of our current 365!

- The T-rex is closer in history to us than to the stegosaurus! While we might think that all dinosaurs existed at the same time, this is far from the truth. The stegosaurus roamed the Earth around 150 million years ago, while Tyrannosaurus rex didn't even exist until only about 66 million years ago. This gives us an 84 million-year difference between the two dinosaur species.

➡ The first dinosaur bone, discovered in 1677 by Robert Plot, was originally thought to belong to a giant human. William Buckland, the geology professor at Oxford University, was the one who correctly identified this historic find as the bone of a long-deceased dinosaur.

➡ The very first Olympic Games were held in the year 776 BC, according to known records, and only one event was included – a footrace. Other events like wrestling, equestrian, discus and jumping were added in later editions of the Games.

➡ Can you imagine watching the Olympic Games today if all the athletes performed their sports naked? Well, in the ancient Olympic Games, that's exactly what happened! This was a regular practice in the Games due to the belief that being naked helped to ascend the competitors' performance and bring them closer to the gods.

- Ever played tug-of-war? This fun and competitive sport of strength was actually an official sporting event at the Olympic Games from 1900 to 1920! It was once included in the track-and-field athletics programme!

- Did you know that fine arts were once a part of the Olympic Games? That's right – from 1912 to 1952, gold medals were awarded in categories of literature, architecture, music, painting and even sculpture! The art that was created had to be Olympic themed.

- We know that the Aztec Empire is an ancient civilisation, so it's pretty astonishing to think that the University of Oxford opened its doors almost 300 years before the Aztec Empire was founded! The institution began its monumental history of educating students back in 1096, while the Aztec Empire began with the building of its capital Tenochtitlán much later, in 1325.

- Chocolate has been around for hundreds of years. The Mayans were already eating it back in the year 600 BC! They are believed to be the first civilisation to mix cacao beans with water, honey, chilli peppers and cornmeal to make a delicious early form of chocolate, according to an archaeological discovery in Belize that indicated residue from this mixture left on some very old ceramic moulds.

- While many believe that the ancient Maya civilisation simply disappeared overnight, this is actually untrue. The vibrant, sophisticated civilisation that existed from 1500 BC to AD 900 actually experienced a gradual decline due to environmental changes, such as long drought periods and deforestation. They were also strained by overpopulation and warfare. Today, you can still meet Maya people.

- Did you know that ketchup used to be sold as a common medicine? There were many varieties of ketchup made from many different kinds of things, including anchovies and oysters! Some of these were believed to cure all kinds of ailments back in the 1830s, such as indigestion, jaundice and diarrhoea! It was even sold in pill form.

PHARAOH BEARDS AND INDESTRUCTIBLE HONEY

- Toothpaste is an invention that's been around for many years. It was invented by the ancient Egyptians, who made the early version of this paste out of salt, pepper, mint and dried flowers. They found white teeth to be a sign of health, beauty and youthfulness.

- The now-extinct woolly mammoths were alive during the time when pyramids were being built in Egypt. The ancient woolly elephants were still alive on a remote Arctic island until about the year 2000 BC, and the Great Pyramid at Giza was assembled around the year 2560 BC. I am not sure if this proves that mammoths aren't as long-gone as we thought, or if the Great Pyramids are much older than we thought – maybe both!

- Did you know, in ancient Egypt, when they mummified people, they carefully removed and preserved organs to keep them safe for ever? But as they believed that the heart was doing all the thinking, they threw the brain away! I guess there was no use for it in the afterlife after all.

- Having a beard in ancient Egypt was considered a sign of godliness, so pharaohs (even females) would often wear false ones tied to their chins with cords.

- Until the construction of Lincoln Cathedral in England in the fourteenth century, Egypt's famous Great Pyramid of Giza was hailed as the tallest structure built by man. It held this title for over 3,800 years!

- The common misconception is to think that the ancient Egyptian pyramids were built by slaves. We know for a fact they were built by skilled labourers who were paid for their work.

- Honey can never spoil. Indeed, archaeologists have discovered honey pots hidden in ancient Egyptian tombs that date back

3,000 years. The honey contained within is still perfectly edible!

- Did you know that Sudan has even more pyramids than Egypt? Indeed, there are also several other countries that are home to famous pyramids, including Mexico, Peru and regions of Asia. However, with over 200 pyramids, Sudan actually has the most of any country.

- The Rosetta Stone was discovered when Napoleon invaded Egypt. It was key to decoding ancient Egyptian hieroglyphics because the inscriptions on the Rosetta Stone say the same thing in three different scripts. Scholars could read the ancient Greek script, and so were able to work out the meaning of hieroglyphs too.

➡ Alexander the Great, the ancient Greek king of Macedon, named more than 70 cities across the globe after himself. Alexandria in Egypt is arguably the most famous example of these, as it went on to become one of the most significant cultural hubs of the ancient Mediterranean world. He also named one city, Bucephala in Pakistan, after his horse, Bucephalus.

- Elephants played an important role in Alexander the Great's conquests. These large mammals were used as medieval tanks, disrupting enemy formations and riling up panic during battles.

- With territories on every continent throughout the course of history, the British Empire is the largest empire the world has ever known. When it was at its most powerful, this empire covered about a quarter of the world's land!

- Archaeological finds suggest that Vikings were conscious of personal hygiene. Ancient tweezers, razors, combs and even animal bones that were made into ear cleaners have been discovered. It is also believed that a special type of soap was created in Scandinavia and exported to other parts of the world, indicating that personal cleanliness was valued by the Vikings.

- ➡ Today, we associate the swastika with the violence and oppression exercised by the Nazi Party in Germany during the twentieth century. However, it was frequently used in many cultures over thousands of years, long before Hitler came into power. Ancient artefacts found in India, Greece, Rome and African regions display this symbol, which was previously associated with good luck, well-being and good fortune.

- ➡ Tulips were once used as a form of currency in the Netherlands. During the 1630s, 'Tulip Mania' erupted across the country, and the flowers became incredibly valuable. Some bulbs even sold for the same value as a whole house! Dutch people would go so far as to trade their land, life savings and homes in exchange for tulip bulbs.

- ➡ Famously one of the world's greatest super-powers, the USSR did not survive for long before it collapsed. Also known as the Soviet Union, the USSR was established in 1922 and gathered 15 republics. It was also incredibly vast, spanning over one-sixth of the Earth's total land surface and covering 11 time zones. However, after political unrest and social reform, the superpower dissolved in 1991.

- The Tsar Bomba was the largest nuclear bomb ever detonated. The Soviet Union set off this weapon of mass destruction in 1961 over the remote Arctic archipelago Novaya Zemlya. The intense blast equalled 3,000 times the strength of the bomb that devastated Hiroshima during the Second World War, and the resulting shockwave circled the entire planet three times!

- For a brief period, the capital of Portugal was actually in Brazil. In 1808, the Portuguese royal court left Europe after threats from Napoleon's armies during the Peninsular War, and established themselves, instead, in Rio de Janeiro. It stayed that way for over a decade until the royal court returned to Lisbon in 1821. This was the only time in history when the capital of a European country was outside of Europe.

- Hidden inside jars and tucked away in 11 caves surrounding the Dead Sea, the so-called Dead Sea Scrolls were discovered in 1947. The ancient texts were over 2,000 years old and also included the very earliest known copies of the Hebrew Bible, allowing us to learn a great deal about the past. Read on to discover how you too can create your own time capsule for people in the future to find.

ACTIVITY: CREATE YOUR OWN TIME CAPSULE

Wow, who knew that history was hiding so many surprises? While the historical events you've just learned about occurred a long time ago, it's never too late to start recording your own history for people of the future to one day look back on. Creating a time capsule as a family can be a great activity to do together – from finding and creating items to place in the capsule to setting an opening date that you all can look forward to and finally opening the capsule together someday in the future!

Instructions

1. It's important to choose a durable container to hold all the time capsule items. You'll want to use something that won't get easily damaged or break down over time. It is best to use a waterproof, airtight container. Your best option would be either a stainless steel box or a thick plastic container. Consider adding an extra layer of protection like a ziplock bag.
2. Now, it's time to select the items you want to put in your time capsule. Try to choose items

that you believe are significant to the present time and that people in the future may find interesting. As you select each item, discuss with one another why you believe it is significant or how it may be helpful to people of the future in understanding your current way of life.

Here are ideas:

- photographs
- coins
- small toys
- your schoolwork or artwork
- a map of your city or neighbourhood
- newspaper and magazine

3. As you go through the process of collecting and selecting items for the capsule, it's fun to make predictions about how future generations may interpret these items.
4. When all the items have been gathered and placed into the capsule, have everyone in the group write a letter to the people who will one day uncover their items. You should include

your hopes, thoughts and feelings about life currently and what the future may hold.

5. Now, it's time to bury your capsule in a safe place. Make sure you seal it so that no air or water can penetrate the container, and find a secure location to bury it. Make sure to somehow mark the spot where you've buried it so that you can easily find it at a later date.
6. Lastly, together select a date and time when the capsule should be uncovered. This can be an important date, such as your eighteenth birthday or 20 years from today. This will give you all something to look forward to. One day, you can all come together again and celebrate the unearthing of the capsule!

LOOK AT THAT VAN GO!

Art, yarn bombing
and robot rock bands

- An experiment conducted in Switzerland attempted to find out if exposing cheese to different types of music while it aged would impact its eventual flavour! The results from this unusual experiment determined that cheese exposed to hip-hop music produced a stronger, fruitier flavour.

- Did you know that there's a music band where all the members are robots? It is called Compressor-head, and it fuses art and technology in a very unique way. Animatronic robots were built from recycled parts and have been programmed to play real musical instruments! They commonly play heavy-metal music – no surprises there!

- What is the smallest piece of art you've ever seen? Well, if you didn't need a microscope to view it, then it couldn't have been as small as the famous artworks painstakingly created by Willard Wigan. He creates sculptures that are so minute, viewers need to look through a micro-scope to admire them. He once even inhaled a piece of a sculpture he was creating – Alice, from *Alice in Wonderland*! Luckily, the piece was remade even better the second time around.

- Yarn bombing, also known as guerrilla knitting or yarn graffiti, is a form of street art where artists cover public spaces with colourful knitted or crocheted yarn. Trees, lamp posts and even statues become vibrant and cosy with these yarn installations.

- The earliest known art piece was created more than 40,000 years ago! These cave paintings depicted pigs, horses and lions in what is now known as the Chauvet-Pont-d'Arc Cave in France. They are believed to have been painted by the Aurignacians, the earliest modern humans to occupy Europe.

- The *Mona Lisa* painting wasn't famous until it was stolen in 1911. By this time, the painting had already existed for over 350 years but had never really caught the attention of people outside the art world. It was later discovered that Vincenzo Peruggia, an Italian museum worker, had stolen the painting with the intention of returning it to its home country of Italy. In the end, however, da Vinci would probably have been glad the theft happened, as it ultimately led to the global fame of the art piece that has become the most recognisable painting in the world today!

- Did you know that you can write letters to the *Mona Lisa*? The woman famously painted by Leonardo da Vinci has her very own mailbox where admirers can send love letters, flowers and poems. Her mysterious smile has been said to enchant many over the years. The name of the painting translates as 'My Lady Lisa', and the woman in the painting is thought to be Lisa Gherardini. So make sure you use her correct name to address her in your letter! You can mail it to: Musée du Louvre, Rue de Rivoli, 75001 Paris, France.

- At one point in time, the *Mona Lisa* was removed from the Louvre Museum in France so that it could hang in the bedroom of French emperor Napoleon. It remained there for four years.

- Did you know that Leonardo da Vinci was ambidextrous? This means that he could write efficiently with both his left and right hands. He could even write with one hand while simultaneously drawing with the other!

- Salvador Dalí believed for most of his life that he was the reincarnation of his older brother, also named Salvador, who died roughly nine months before the artist's birth. He even featured images of his older brother in a few of his paintings, such as *Portrait of My Dead Brother*.

- One of Banksy's famous paintings, *Girl with Balloon*, iconically self-destructed in 2018 mere moments after it was sold for a whopping £1 million. When displayed at the auction, and unbeknown to the bidders, the frame of the painting was secretly fitted with a shredder that was activated remotely as soon as the sale of the art piece was confirmed. However, art experts estimate that the 'half-destroyed' artwork has actually doubled in value since this public stunt.

- It's sad to think about, but the world-famous and globally admired artist Van Gogh sold only one painting in his lifetime. It is widely known that he struggled and never really received the attention his talent deserved. That one painting was sold for 400 francs in Brussels, just a few months before the artist passed away.

- There are actually four different versions of the famous *The Scream* painting. The artist, Edvard Munch, painted the original version in 1893 and went on to create a pastel version later the same year. The third version was sold to a private buyer, and the fourth was given to the Munch Museum to be displayed to the public.

- The colour wheel that we use to match complementary colour palettes has been assisting creators for over 300 years! The wheel was invented by Isaac Newton in 1666 by refracting pure white sunlight into six different colours. His discovery that this refraction of light created the different colours we know was revolutionary at the time.

- An innovative technique of piano playing, invented by a famous composer of the twentieth century, John Cage, is called 'prepared piano'. Cage placed objects such as screws, pieces of kitchen foil and rubber ducks onto the strings of a piano and noted the new sounds that could be made when it was played. This astonishing technique allowed Cage to produce music no one had ever heard before!

- The Father of the Symphony, Austrian composer Joseph Haydn, strangely has two skulls in his tomb. While this may seem mysterious and slightly ominous, there's a fair explanation. Someone actually broke into the tomb and stole his skull after his death in 1809, so his family replaced it with a temporary one until the thief was caught. However, when the real skull was later recovered and returned to the tomb in 1954, the replacement skull remained.

- The peak of Elvis Presley's musical career might have happened back in the 1950s and 1960s, but with half a billion sales worldwide, the king of rock 'n' roll is still the number one selling solo artist of all time and is yet to be outdone by the popular artists of today.

- In August 2015, the world record for the longest drumming marathon by an individual was achieved by Canadian drummer Steve Gaul. He played for an astounding 134 hours and 5 minutes without stopping, to raise money for charity.

- The oldest known musical composition in the world is the Seikilos Epitaph. It was found written on a column that formed a grave in Turkey, and it is believed to date back to the year AD 100. It includes lyrics and a musical score.

- As part of the London Palladium's Music is Magic concert in 2017, the largest-ever triangle ensemble was performed by David Stanley and The Music Man Project. This magnificent collective consisted of 1,521 triangle players, all performing together!

- She may be lesser known, but Mozart's sister was also incredibly talented. Maria Anna Mozart was known to play the piano equally as well as her gifted brother. Mozart and 'Nannerl', as she was nicknamed, even played in multiple cities across Europe as child prodigies. As it was the eighteenth century, however, Nannerl's career as a budding musician came to a close when she became old enough for marriage.

- Did you know that listening to Mozart is believed to boost your brain's ability to solve complex puzzles? The 'Mozart Effect', first proposed in the

1990s, is a popular theory stating that listening to the composer's music regularly can improve a person's spatial-temporal abilities, allowing them to solve puzzles and reason with shapes more easily. While the publication of the theory originally boosted sales of Mozart's music, later research delivered a mix of results. While it may still be uncertain, the theory does make me think about a fascinating link between music and our mental capabilities.

- The term 'don't play with your food' was widely disregarded by a unique musical group based in Vienna, Austria, known as the Vegetable Orchestra. They create compositions by playing instruments entirely made from vegetables such as carrots, pumpkins and peppers! And the fresh vegetables don't go to waste – after every performance, they are cooked into a vegetable soup, which the group shares with their audience.

- The Sea Organ located in Zadar, Croatia, is a uniquely built instrument that is played by the waves of the sea! This famous set of pipes is actually built into the steps of the coastline.

Waves crashing up against it expel air through the pipes of the organ so that a range of musical sounds are produced. These sounds can be heard through holes made in the pavement, creating a harmonious symphony for everyone to enjoy.

➡ The world's largest instrument is a massive organ located in the Luray Caverns of Virginia, USA. The Great Stalacpipe Organ covers about 15,000 square metres of the enormous cave, and it is made of rubber mallets that rhythmically tap icicle-shaped formations hanging from the ceiling of the cave to produce musical notes.

➡ Did you know that the famous composer Beethoven was almost entirely deaf by the time he reached his mid-forties? He began to lose his hearing in his late twenties, but despite this significant setback, he went on to compose some of his most iconic symphonies when he could barely hear at all. In fact, despite his deafness, he insisted that he conduct the opening premiere of his famous Symphony No. 9. Witnesses have said that he continued conducting the orchestra even after they had ceased playing, as he couldn't hear the audience applauding.

- Many musical composers have used non-traditional items, besides their usual musical instruments, to create unusual sounds for their compositions. For example, David Lang used damaged instruments from public schools in Philadelphia for his piece, *Symphony for a Broken Orchestra.* Sirens, anvils and a wind machine were used by Edgar Varèse in his piece, *Ionisation*, and George Crumb employed the use of crystal glasses and thimbles for his composition, *Black Angels.*

- There are several 'musical roads' across the world that have been designed to create music when you drive over them in a car at a specific speed. As the wheels of a car move over grooves cut into the road's surface, they cause vibrations that produce tunes. You can hear the music from within the car as well as from the road, creating a highly unique driving experience! What a melodious way to encourage drivers not to go over the speed limit!

- Madhubani is a famous art style originating in Bihar, India, that has decreased deforestation! Several artists gathered together in 2012 to create art pieces on the trunks of trees growing along a highway in the Madhubani district, in an attempt to discourage people from chopping down the trees. It actually worked – not a single painted tree was chopped! This area now attracts many tourists and brings awareness to the issue of deforestation.

- Not only is art an essential form of self-expression and creativity, but it also contributes significantly to the economy. The worldwide art market was valued at more than 67.8 billion US dollars in 2022! This includes economic contributions from the industries of painting, sculpture, photography, NFTs and others.

- Jan van Eyck's painting *The Arnolfini Portrait* displays its artist's reflection in a small mirror at the centre of the canvas. In Rembrandt's famous painting *The Night Watch*, the artist actually features in the background of the painting – you can only see his eye and beret, but he's there!

Follow the instructions at the end of the chapter to create a deceptive work of art featuring your own hand.

ACTIVITY: TURN YOUR HAND INTO AN OPTICAL ILLUSION

It's time to let your inner artist shine through with a fun and engaging activity that's suitable for all ages. You can enjoy it by yourself or turn it into a family-time activity. Drawing a 3D image can look daunting and difficult, but this next challenge shows you how easy it can be.

Materials

- A piece of paper
- A ruler
- A pencil
- Your hand
- Any colouring materials (crayons, coloured pencils, markers, etc.)

Instructions

1. First, place your hand in the centre of the paper and use a pencil to trace around it.
2. Using a ruler, draw straight, horizontal lines from one side of the paper to the other. Make sure not to allow the lines to cross over your hand tracing – so imagine that your hand is at the front and the lines are behind it. The lines should be equal distances apart – about 1 cm.
3. Draw curved lines inside your hand tracing, with each curved line connecting to a straight line outside the hand tracing. It might help to use your ruler, lining it up against each straight line one at a time. That way, you can see where the ends of each curved line need to connect to its corresponding straight line. The end result should be straight lines going across the page outside of the hand tracing, with the lines appearing to curve 'over' the hand that you've traced.
4. Colour each section created by the lines. Each line should be a different colour. Try creating a pattern or just use a random colour for each

line. With a splash of colour, you'll now start to see the illusion of your 3D hand coming to life!

Take it further

For a more realistic 3D effect, try adding shades with a pencil along one side of the hand and fingers. You can use this technique to turn other objects into 3D illusions too.

IT'S A WRAP, BRAIN-WAVERS!

But We've Only
Scratched the Surface . . .

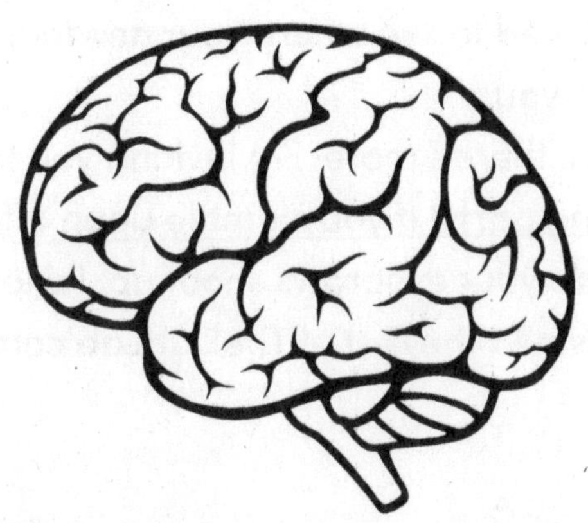

Well, my friend, here you are at the end of the book, but only at the beginning of an extraordinary journey of discovery that I hope this book has inspired.

Our expedition began as a quest for fun, and oh boy, I hope you had plenty of it! But if you take one thing from this book, let it be that we are never done learning. Even though you have just gobbled up an astounding array of facts, the universe remains an infinite buffet of knowledge waiting for you to sample! There are always more questions to be asked, more phenomena to observe, and more places in time and space to explore. The knowledge you can acquire truly has no limits!

So, I challenge you to keep exploring and keep having fun. After all, the greatest adventures begin with a single spark of curiosity.

Thank you for joining me on this adventure. I hope it's been as thrilling for you as it has for me, and I'm excited to see where your newfound knowledge leads you.

But wait, there's more! I'm inviting you to join the fact-hunting party! If you stumble upon a fact so cool it made your eyebrows shoot up, I'd love to hear it, and so would the rest of TheDadLab community!

Submit your facts on our website at www.thedadlab.com/facts, or share them on social media by tagging @thedadlab and using the hashtag #thedadlab. Because when it comes to learning, the more the merrier!

Keep exploring,
Sergei

SCAN AND SHARE YOUR AMAZING FACTS!

ACKNOWLEDGEMENTS

First and foremost, a shoutout to all curious minds out there. Keep those questions coming! Let's never stop being amazed by the world around us. A big thank you to YOU, my reader!

Thank you to my children, who have been my fearless lab assistants and partners in mess-making. Thanks for enduring my occasional explosive experiments and for asking 'Why?' a million times. You're the reason I do what I do. To my amazing wife Tania, who's not only my better half but also the patient one. You're my anchor in this whirlwind.

To all the animals, plants, rocks and stars that make our world a mind-blowing place: your odd behaviours, complex ecosystems and strange phenomena are the reason we have a book full of wild facts to begin with.

To all the science teachers who ignite the spark of curiosity in us, thank you. You show us that SCIENCE is an adventure waiting to happen. I hope this book captures a fraction of the enthusiasm you instill in us.

To my neighbours, who kindly pretended not to notice the strange noises, occasional bangs and mysterious glows coming from our house. We promise we're not building a doomsday device – just trying to figure out how to make the best slime!

To my literary agent Kathleen Ortiz, the keeper of my wild ideas. Thank you for putting up with my creative chaos and supporting me through it all. You're the true mastermind behind the madness.

And finally, to my co-conspirator in this fact-finding frenzy, my editor Beth Eynon, thank you for joining me on this wild ride. Who knew that our shared curiosity and a good laugh could lead to a book?

With endless curiosity and gratitude,

Sergei Urban